My Book
of
Centuries

by Christie Groff & Sonya Shafer

My Book of Centuries, Second Edition
© 2014 by Christie Groff and Sonya Shafer

Cover Design: John Shafer

ISBN 978-1-61634-248-7 printed
ISBN 978-1-61634-249-4 electronic download

Published by
Simply Charlotte Mason, LLC
930 New Hope Road #11-892
Lawrenceville, Georgia 30045
simplycharlottemason.com

Printed by PrintLogic, Inc.
Monroe, Georgia, USA

A Book of Centuries is one of those things that has been on my to-do list since I quit doing a wall timeline in late 2009. I've printed a couple, tried my hand at them as a family project, and fizzled. I tried to add every interesting figure and event and fretted over leaving something out. In reality, I was overcomplicating the whole process! As a result, I set about learning more about how Charlotte Mason dealt with the issue of chronicling time. I discovered that this keeping of time should be a delight and not a burden and that there are many interpretations of the best way to achieve that goal - wall timeline, timeline in a book or on the computer, or a book of centuries. No two books should be exactly alike, but rather each keeper of time should personalize his book by chronicling those events, people, and moments how he sees fit. This book is my own attempt at doing so. I hope that you will find it useful as you begin your own journey to chronicle time.

– Christie

P.S.
This 2nd edition condenses the content of the original, keeping all of the elements, but shortening each century to a single two-page spread. This is more in line with how Charlotte's students marked time and most importantly to me, it makes the book thinner, more portable, and less unwieldy.

Sample Pages
20th Century A.D.

Noteworthy

Art, Music, & Prominent Men & Women	Events, Wars, Movements & Ideas	Developments, Discoveries & Inventions	Authors, Poets & Period Literature
• President Ronald Reagan • Billy Graham • Ansel Adams • Norman Rockwell • Georgia O'Keefe • John Williams • Louis Armstrong • Sir Winston Churchill • Marie Curie • Amelia Earhart • Elvis Presley • Sigmund Freud • Henry Ford • Cubism art movement	• Operation Desert Shield • Operation Desert Storm • Washington March for Jesus • Great Depression • Cold War • Civil Rights Movement • Tiananmen Square • Existentialism	• Post-It Notes • Cell Phones • MRI • Walkmans • Video Games • Internet • Apple Mac Computer • Space Travel • High Speed Railroad	• _The Journey that Saved Curious George_ by Borden • A.A. Milne • C.S. Lewis • J.R.R. Tolkien • _The Great Gatsby_ by F. Scott Fitzgerald • _Anne of Green Gables_ by Lucy Maude Montgomery • Ernest Hemingway • Faulkner • E. Nesbit • _The Call of the Wild_

Century Artifacts

Century at a Glance

	5
	10
	15
	20
	25
Stock Market Crash Great Depression	30
Great Depression Great Depression Great Depression	35
	40
	45
	50
	55
	60
President Kennedy Assassinated	65
	70
Christie G. Born	75
Dominica Gains Independence	80
	85
Berlin Wall Falls Operation Desert Storm	90
Operation Desert Storm	95
Y2K Fear	100

Brief Narrative of Century

The twentieth century was a time of marked technological advances. Things not dreamed of were invented and improved upon at a rapid-fire pace...

Helpful Articles, Templates, and Tidbits

- *The Book of Centuries* by Mrs. G.M. Barnau
  from *The Parent's Review,* Volume 34 (1923), pp. 720–724

- *The Book of Centuries Revisited* by Laurie Bestvater
  at http://childlightusa.wordpress.com

- *The Teaching of Chronology* by Dorothea Beale
  from *The Parent's Review,* Volume 2 (1891–92), pp. 81–90

- *Book of Centuries Q & A* by Sonya Shafer
  on *YouTube.com*

- Book of Centuries template
  available at *SimplyCharlotteMason.com*

- *How and When to Begin a Book of Centuries*
  at www.charlottemasonhelp.com

- P.N.E.U. student examples
  at http://charlottemason.redeemer.ca/PNEU-Briefcase/PNEU-Box24/pneu162/i3p43-p86pneu162.pdf
  and
  http://charlottemason.redeemer.ca/PNEU-Briefcase/PNEU-Box24/pneu162/i3p01-p42pneu162.pdf

There is a plethora of information out there. Do some snooping and find more that's helpful to you!

B.C.

Early Artifacts

Early Beginnings

30th Century B.C.

Noteworthy

Art, Music & Prominent Men & Women	Events, Wars, Movements & Ideas	Developments, Discoveries & Inventions	Authors, Poets & Period Literature

Century Artifacts

Century at a Glance

100				
95				
90				
85				
80				
75				
70				
65				
60				
55				
50				
45				
40				
35				
30				
25				
20				
15				
10				
5				

Brief Narrative of Century

29th Century B.C.

Noteworthy

Art, Music & Prominent Men & Women	Events, Wars, Movements & Ideas	Developments, Discoveries & Inventions	Authors, Poets & Period Literature

Century Artifacts

Century at a Glance

100					
95					
90					
85					
80					
75					
70					
65					
60					
55					
50					
45					
40					
35					
30					
25					
20					
15					
10					
5					

Brief Narrative of Century

28th Century B.C.

Art, Music & Prominent Men & Women	Events, Wars, Movements & Ideas	Developments, Discoveries & Inventions	Authors, Poets & Period Literature

Century Artifacts

Century at a Glance

100				
95				
90				
85				
80				
75				
70				
65				
60				
55				
50				
45				
40				
35				
30				
25				
20				
15				
10				
5				

Brief Narrative of Century

27th Century B.C.

Art, Music & Prominent Men & Women	Events, Wars, Movements & Ideas	Developments, Discoveries & Inventions	Authors, Poets & Period Literature

Century Artifacts

Century at a Glance

100					
95					
90					
85					
80					
75					
70					
65					
60					
55					
50					
45					
40					
35					
30					
25					
20					
15					
10					
5					

Brief Narrative of Century

26th Century B.C.

Art, Music & Prominent Men & Women	Events, Wars, Movements & Ideas	Developments, Discoveries & Inventions	Authors, Poets & Period Literature

Century Artifacts

Century at a Glance

100				
95				
90				
85				
80				
75				
70				
65				
60				
55				
50				
45				
40				
35				
30				
25				
20				
15				
10				
5				

Brief Narrative of Century

25th Century B.C.

Noteworthy

Art, Music & Prominent Men & Women	Events, Wars, Movements & Ideas	Developments, Discoveries & Inventions	Authors, Poets & Period Literature

Century Artifacts

Century at a Glance

	100				
95					
90					
85					
80					
75					
70					
65					
60					
55					
50					
45					
40					
35					
30					
25					
20					
15					
10					
5					

Brief Narrative of Century

24th Century B.C.

Noteworthy

Art, Music & Prominent Men & Women	Events, Wars, Movements & Ideas	Developments, Discoveries & Inventions	Authors, Poets & Period Literature

Century Artifacts

Century at a Glance

100				
95				
90				
85				
80				
75				
70				
65				
60				
55				
50				
45				
40				
35				
30				
25				
20				
15				
10				
5				

Brief Narrative of Century

23rd Century B.C.

Art, Music & Prominent Men & Women	Events, Wars, Movements & Ideas	Developments, Discoveries & Inventions	Authors, Poets & Period Literature

Century Artifacts

Century at a Glance

100					
95					
90					
85					
80					
75					
70					
65					
60					
55					
50					
45					
40					
35					
30					
25					
20					
15					
10					
5					

Brief Narrative of Century

22nd Century B.C.

Noteworthy

Art, Music & Prominent Men & Women	Events, Wars, Movements & Ideas	Developments, Discoveries & Inventions	Authors, Poets & Period Literature

Century Artifacts

Century at a Glance

100					
95					
90					
85					
80					
75					
70					
65					
60					
55					
50					
45					
40					
35					
30					
25					
20					
15					
10					
5					

Brief Narrative of Century

21st Century B.C.

Noteworthy

Art, Music & Prominent Men & Women	Events, Wars, Movements & Ideas	Developments, Discoveries & Inventions	Authors, Poets & Period Literature

Century Artifacts

Century at a Glance

100					
95					
90					
85					
80					
75					
70					
65					
60					
55					
50					
45					
40					
35					
30					
25					
20					
15					
10					
5					

Brief Narrative of Century

20th Century B.C.

Art, Music & Prominent Men & Women	Events, Wars, Movements & Ideas	Developments, Discoveries & Inventions	Authors, Poets & Period Literature

Century Artifacts

Century at a Glance

100				
95				
90				
85				
80				
75				
70				
65				
60				
55				
50				
45				
40				
35				
30				
25				
20				
15				
10				
5				

Brief Narrative of Century

19th Century B.C.

Noteworthy

Art, Music & Prominent Men & Women	Events, Wars, Movements & Ideas	Developments, Discoveries & Inventions	Authors, Poets & Period Literature

Century Artifacts

Century at a Glance

100				
95				
90				
85				
80				
75				
70				
65				
60				
55				
50				
45				
40				
35				
30				
25				
20				
15				
10				
5				

Brief Narrative of Century

18th Century B.C.

Noteworthy

Art, Music & Prominent Men & Women	Events, Wars, Movements & Ideas	Developments, Discoveries & Inventions	Authors, Poets & Period Literature

Century Artifacts

Century at a Glance

100					
95					
90					
85					
80					
75					
70					
65					
60					
55					
50					
45					
40					
35					
30					
25					
20					
15					
10					
5					

Brief Narrative of Century

17th Century B.C.

Art, Music & Prominent Men & Women	Events, Wars, Movements & Ideas	Developments, Discoveries & Inventions	Authors, Poets & Period Literature

Century Artifacts

Century at a Glance

100				
95				
90				
85				
80				
75				
70				
65				
60				
55				
50				
45				
40				
35				
30				
25				
20				
15				
10				
5				

Brief Narrative of Century

16th Century B.C.

Art, Music & Prominent Men & Women	Events, Wars, Movements & Ideas	Developments, Discoveries & Inventions	Authors, Poets & Period Literature

Century Artifacts

Century at a Glance

100				
95				
90				
85				
80				
75				
70				
65				
60				
55				
50				
45				
40				
35				
30				
25				
20				
15				
10				
5				

Brief Narrative of Century

15th Century B.C.

Art, Music & Prominent Men & Women	Events, Wars, Movements & Ideas	Developments, Discoveries & Inventions	Authors, Poets & Period Literature

Century Artifacts

Century at a Glance

100				
95				
90				
85				
80				
75				
70				
65				
60				
55				
50				
45				
40				
35				
30				
25				
20				
15				
10				
5				

Brief Narrative of Century

14th Century B.C.

Art, Music & Prominent Men & Women	Events, Wars, Movements & Ideas	Developments, Discoveries & Inventions	Authors, Poets & Period Literature

Century Artifacts

Century at a Glance

100				
95				
90				
85				
80				
75				
70				
65				
60				
55				
50				
45				
40				
35				
30				
25				
20				
15				
10				
5				

Brief Narrative of Century

13th Century B.C.

Art, Music & Prominent Men & Women	Events, Wars, Movements & Ideas	Developments, Discoveries & Inventions	Authors, Poets & Period Literature

Century Artifacts

Century at a Glance

100					
95					
90					
85					
80					
75					
70					
65					
60					
55					
50					
45					
40					
35					
30					
25					
20					
15					
10					
5					

Brief Narrative of Century

12th Century B.C.

Art, Music & Prominent Men & Women	Events, Wars, Movements & Ideas	Developments, Discoveries & Inventions	Authors, Poets & Period Literature

Century Artifacts

Century at a Glance

100				
95				
90				
85				
80				
75				
70				
65				
60				
55				
50				
45				
40				
35				
30				
25				
20				
15				
10				
5				

Brief Narrative of Century

11th Century B.C.

Noteworthy

Art, Music & Prominent Men & Women	Events, Wars, Movements & Ideas	Developments, Discoveries & Inventions	Authors, Poets & Period Literature

Century Artifacts

Century at a Glance

100				
95				
90				
85				
80				
75				
70				
65				
60				
55				
50				
45				
40				
35				
30				
25				
20				
15				
10				
5				

Brief Narrative of Century

10th Century B.C.

Noteworthy

Art, Music & Prominent Men & Women	Events, Wars, Movements & Ideas	Developments, Discoveries & Inventions	Authors, Poets & Period Literature

Century Artifacts

Century at a Glance

100				
95				
90				
85				
80				
75				
70				
65				
60				
55				
50				
45				
40				
35				
30				
25				
20				
15				
10				
5				

Brief Narrative of Century

9th Century B.C.

Noteworthy

Art, Music & Prominent Men & Women	Events, Wars, Movements & Ideas	Developments, Discoveries & Inventions	Authors, Poets & Period Literature

Century Artifacts

Century at a Glance

100				
95				
90				
85				
80				
75				
70				
65				
60				
55				
50				
45				
40				
35				
30				
25				
20				
15				
10				
5				

Brief Narrative of Century

8th Century B.C.

Noteworthy

Art, Music & Prominent Men & Women	Events, Wars, Movements & Ideas	Developments, Discoveries & Inventions	Authors, Poets & Period Literature

Century Artifacts

Century at a Glance

100				
95				
90				
85				
80				
75				
70				
65				
60				
55				
50				
45				
40				
35				
30				
25				
20				
15				
10				
5				

Brief Narrative of Century

7th Century B.C.

Noteworthy

Art, Music & Prominent Men & Women	Events, Wars, Movements & Ideas	Developments, Discoveries & Inventions	Authors, Poets & Period Literature

Century Artifacts

Century at a Glance

100					
95					
90					
85					
80					
75					
70					
65					
60					
55					
50					
45					
40					
35					
30					
25					
20					
15					
10					
5					

Brief Narrative of Century

6th Century B.C.

Noteworthy

Art, Music & Prominent Men & Women	Events, Wars, Movements & Ideas	Developments, Discoveries & Inventions	Authors, Poets & Period Literature

Century Artifacts

Century at a Glance

	100				
	95				
	90				
	85				
	80				
	75				
	70				
	65				
	60				
	55				
	50				
	45				
	40				
	35				
	30				
	25				
	20				
	15				
	10				
	5				

Brief Narrative of Century

5th Century B.C.

Noteworthy

Art, Music & Prominent Men & Women	Events, Wars, Movements & Ideas	Developments, Discoveries & Inventions	Authors, Poets & Period Literature

Century Artifacts

Century at a Glance

100				
95				
90				
85				
80				
75				
70				
65				
60				
55				
50				
45				
40				
35				
30				
25				
20				
15				
10				
5				

Brief Narrative of Century

4th Century B.C.

Art, Music & Prominent Men & Women	Events, Wars, Movements & Ideas	Developments, Discoveries & Inventions	Authors, Poets & Period Literature

Century Artifacts

Century at a Glance

100				
95				
90				
85				
80				
75				
70				
65				
60				
55				
50				
45				
40				
35				
30				
25				
20				
15				
10				
5				

Brief Narrative of Century

3rd Century B.C.

Noteworthy

Art, Music & Prominent Men & Women	Events, Wars, Movements & Ideas	Developments, Discoveries & Inventions	Authors, Poets & Period Literature

Century Artifacts

Century at a Glance

100					
95					
90					
85					
80					
75					
70					
65					
60					
55					
50					
45					
40					
35					
30					
25					
20					
15					
10					
5					

Brief Narrative of Century

2nd Century B.C.

Noteworthy

Art, Music & Prominent Men & Women	Events, Wars, Movements & Ideas	Developments, Discoveries & Inventions	Authors, Poets & Period Literature

Century Artifacts

Century at a Glance

100					
95					
90					
85					
80					
75					
70					
65					
60					
55					
50					
45					
40					
35					
30					
25					
20					
15					
10					
5					

Brief Narrative of Century

1st Century B.C.

Noteworthy

Art, Music & Prominent Men & Women	Events, Wars, Movements & Ideas	Developments, Discoveries & Inventions	Authors, Poets & Period Literature

Century Artifacts

Century at a Glance

100				
95				
90				
85				
80				
75				
70				
65				
60				
55				
50				
45				
40				
35				
30				
25				
20				
15				
10				
5	Jesus was Born - 4 BC			

Brief Narrative of Century

A.D.

1st Century A.D.

Noteworthy

Art, Music & Prominent Men & Women	Events, Wars, Movements & Ideas	Developments, Discoveries & Inventions	Authors, Poets & Period Literature

Century Artifacts

Century at a Glance

	5
	10
	15
	20
	25
Jesus died & ressurection 30 AD Church began	30
	35
	40
	45
	50
	55
	60
	65
	70
	75
	80
	85
	90
	95
	100

Brief Narrative of Century

2nd Century A.D.

Noteworthy

Art, Music & Prominent Men & Women	Events, Wars, Movements & Ideas	Developments, Discoveries & Inventions	Authors, Poets & Period Literature

Century Artifacts

Century at a Glance

	5
	10
	15
	20
	25
	30
	35
	40
	45
	50
	55
	60
	65
	70
	75
	80
	85
	90
	95
	100

Brief Narrative of Century

3rd Century A.D.

Noteworthy

Art, Music & Prominent Men & Women	Events, Wars, Movements & Ideas	Developments, Discoveries & Inventions	Authors, Poets & Period Literature

Century Artifacts

Century at a Glance

	5
	10
	15
	20
	25
	30
	35
	40
	45
	50
	55
	60
	65
	70
	75
	80
	85
	90
	95
	100

Brief Narrative of Century

4th Century A.D.

Noteworthy

Art, Music & Prominent Men & Women	Events, Wars, Movements & Ideas	Developments, Discoveries & Inventions	Authors, Poets & Period Literature

Century Artifacts

Century at a Glance

	5
	10
	15
	20
	25
	30
	35
	40
	45
	50
	55
	60
	65
	70
	75
	80
	85
	90
	95
	100

Brief Narrative of Century

5th Century A.D.

Noteworthy

Art, Music & Prominent Men & Women	Events, Wars, Movements & Ideas	Developments, Discoveries & Inventions	Authors, Poets & Period Literature

Century Artifacts

Century at a Glance

	5
	10
	15
	20
	25
	30
	35
	40
	45
	50
	55
	60
	65
	70
	75
	80
	85
	90
	95
	100

Brief Narrative of Century

6th Century A.D.

Noteworthy

Art, Music & Prominent Men & Women	Events, Wars, Movements & Ideas	Developments, Discoveries & Inventions	Authors, Poets & Period Literature

Century Artifacts

Century at a Glance

	5
	10
	15
	20
	25
	30
	35
	40
	45
	50
	55
	60
	65
	70
	75
	80
	85
	90
	95
	100

Brief Narrative of Century

7th Century A.D.

Art, Music & Prominent Men & Women	Events, Wars, Movements & Ideas	Developments, Discoveries & Inventions	Authors, Poets & Period Literature

Century Artifacts

Century at a Glance

	5
	10
	15
	20
	25
	30
	35
	40
	45
	50
	55
	60
	65
	70
	75
	80
	85
	90
	95
	100

Brief Narrative of Century

8th Century A.D.

Noteworthy

Art, Music & Prominent Men & Women	Events, Wars, Movements & Ideas	Developments, Discoveries & Inventions	Authors, Poets & Period Literature

Century Artifacts

Century at a Glance

	5
	10
	15
	20
	25
	30
	35
	40
	45
	50
	55
	60
	65
	70
	75
	80
	85
	90
	95
	100

Brief Narrative of Century

9th Century A.D.

Noteworthy

Art, Music & Prominent Men & Women	Events, Wars, Movements & Ideas	Developments, Discoveries & Inventions	Authors, Poets & Period Literature

Century Artifacts

Century at a Glance

	5
	10
	15
	20
	25
	30
	35
	40
	45
	50
	55
	60
	65
	70
	75
	80
	85
	90
	95
	100

Brief Narrative of Century

10th Century A.D.

Noteworthy

Art, Music & Prominent Men & Women	Events, Wars, Movements & Ideas	Developments, Discoveries & Inventions	Authors, Poets & Period Literature

Century Artifacts

Century at a Glance

	5
	10
	15
	20
	25
	30
	35
	40
	45
	50
	55
	60
	65
Leif the Lucky Birth 970	70
	75
	80
	85
	90
	95
Leif discovers America - 1000	100

Brief Narrative of Century

11th Century A.D.

Noteworthy

Art, Music & Prominent Men & Women	Events, Wars, Movements & Ideas	Developments, Discoveries & Inventions	Authors, Poets & Period Literature

Century Artifacts

Century at a Glance

	5
	10
	15
	20
	25
	30
	35
	40
	45
	50
	55
	60
	65
	70
	75
	80
	85
	90
	95
	100

Brief Narrative of Century

12th Century A.D.

Noteworthy

Art, Music & Prominent Men & Women	Events, Wars, Movements & Ideas	Developments, Discoveries & Inventions	Authors, Poets & Period Literature

Century Artifacts

Century at a Glance

	5
	10
	15
	20
	25
	30
	35
	40
	45
	50
	55
	60
	65
	70
	75
	80
	85
	90
	95
	100

Brief Narrative of Century

13th Century A.D.

Noteworthy

Art, Music & Prominent Men & Women	Events, Wars, Movements & Ideas	Developments, Discoveries & Inventions	Authors, Poets & Period Literature

Century Artifacts

Century at a Glance

	5
	10
	15
	20
	25
	30
	35
	40
	45
	50
	55
	60
	65
	70
	75
	80
	85
	90
	95
	100

Brief Narrative of Century

14th Century A.D.

Noteworthy

Art, Music & Prominent Men & Women	Events, Wars, Movements & Ideas	Developments, Discoveries & Inventions	Authors, Poets & Period Literature

Century Artifacts

Century at a Glance

	5
	10
	15
	20
	25
	30
	35
	40
	45
	50
	55
	60
	65
	70
	75
	80
	85
	90
	95
	100

Brief Narrative of Century

15th Century A.D.

Noteworthy

Art, Music & Prominent Men & Women	Events, Wars, Movements & Ideas	Developments, Discoveries & Inventions	Authors, Poets & Period Literature

Century Artifacts

Century at a Glance

	5
	10
	15
	20
	25
	30
	35
	40
	45
	50
	55
	60
	65
	70
	75
	80
	85
	90
	95
	100

Brief Narrative of Century

16th Century A.D.

Noteworthy

Art, Music & Prominent Men & Women	Events, Wars, Movements & Ideas	Developments, Discoveries & Inventions	Authors, Poets & Period Literature

Century Artifacts

Century at a Glance

	5
	10
	15
	20
	25
	30
	35
	40
	45
	50
	55
	60
	65
	70
	75
	80
	85
	90
	95
	100

Brief Narrative of Century

17th Century A.D.

Noteworthy

Art, Music & Prominent Men & Women	Events, Wars, Movements & Ideas	Developments, Discoveries & Inventions	Authors, Poets & Period Literature

Century Artifacts

Century at a Glance

	5
	10
	15
	20
	25
	30
	35
	40
	45
	50
	55
	60
	65
	70
	75
	80
	85
	90
	95
	100

Brief Narrative of Century

18th Century A.D.

Noteworthy

Art, Music & Prominent Men & Women	Events, Wars, Movements & Ideas	Developments, Discoveries & Inventions	Authors, Poets & Period Literature

Century Artifacts

Century at a Glance

	5
	10
	15
	20
	25
	30
	35
	40
	45
	50
	55
	60
	65
	70
	75
	80
	85
	90
	95
	100

Brief Narrative of Century

19th Century A.D.

Noteworthy

Art, Music & Prominent Men & Women	Events, Wars, Movements & Ideas	Developments, Discoveries & Inventions	Authors, Poets & Period Literature

Century Artifacts

Century at a Glance

	5
	10
	15
	20
	25
Emily Dickenson Birth - 1830	30
	35
	40
	45
	50
	55
	60
	65
	70
	75
	80
	85
Emily Dickenson Death - 1886	90
	95
	100

Brief Narrative of Century

20th Century A.D.

Noteworthy

Art, Music & Prominent Men & Women	Events, Wars, Movements & Ideas	Developments, Discoveries & Inventions	Authors, Poets & Period Literature

Century Artifacts

Century at a Glance

	5
	10
	15
	20
	25
	30
	35
	40
	45
	50
	55
	60
	65
	70
	75
Momma birthg Daddy's Birth	80
	85
	90
	95
	100

Brief Narrative of Century

21st Century A.D.

Noteworthy

Art, Music & Prominent Men & Women	Events, Wars, Movements & Ideas	Developments, Discoveries & Inventions	Authors, Poets & Period Literature

Century Artifacts

Century at a Glance

Lyla birth - '14
maggie birth -'16

	5
	10
	15
	20
	25
	30
	35
	40
	45
	50
	55
	60
	65
	70
	75
	80
	85
	90
	95
	100

Brief Narrative of Century

22nd Century A.D.

Noteworthy

Art, Music & Prominent Men & Women	Events, Wars, Movements & Ideas	Developments, Discoveries & Inventions	Authors, Poets & Period Literature

Century Artifacts

Century at a Glance

	5
	10
	15
	20
	25
	30
	35
	40
	45
	50
	55
	60
	65
	70
	75
	80
	85
	90
	95
	100

Brief Narrative of Century